ANSWERS TO ODD-NUMBERED PROBLEMS TO ACCOMPANY

PHYSICS FOR SCIENCE AND ENGINEERING

JOHN P. McKELVEY
HOWARD GROTCH

HARPER & ROW, PUBLISHERS

ANSWERS TO ODD-NUMBERED PROBLEMS

TO ACCOMPANY

PHYSICS FOR SCIENCE AND ENGINEERING

John P. McKelvey
Clemson University

Howard Grotch
Pennsylvania State University

HARPER & ROW, PUBLISHERS, Inc.

New York Hagerstown San Francisco London

Answers to Odd-Numbered Problems to accompany
PHYSICS FOR SCIENCE AND ENGINEERING

For information address Harper & Row, Publishers, Inc., 10 East 53rd Street, New York, N.Y. 10022.

ISBN 0-06-364108-9

Chapter 1

7. 20 units, 53°
9. magnitude 8.46 inches, angle with x-axis 47.6°
11. a) -18.4 mi, + 42.4 mi b) 46.25 mi c) 113.5° d) zero
13. magnitude 60.8 miles, makes an angle 25.3° with direction due east
15. C = 82.6 lb, in a direction (in the fourth quadrant) making an angle of -80.7° with the positive x-axis
17. a) 1 unit; b) 3 units; c) $\sqrt{10}$ units; d) 71.6°
19. a) magnitude 91.9 nautical miles, direction 49.2° S of E b) magnitude 61.5 nautical miles, direction 12.8° S of E
23. a) 2, b) $5\mathbf{i}_x + 10\mathbf{i}_y + 5\mathbf{i}_z$
25. $3\mathbf{i}_x - 2\mathbf{i}_y$, or any scalar multiple thereof
27. a) 15 units, 126.9° with x-axis, b) 9.06 units, 6.34° with x-axis, c) 9 units, 1 unit
29. $\mathbf{i}_r = \mathbf{r}/r = \mathbf{i}_x(x/r) + \mathbf{i}_y(y/r) = \mathbf{i}_x(\cos\theta) + \mathbf{i}_y(\sin\theta)$ where θ is the angle r makes with the x-axis
31. -9, $-13\mathbf{i}_z$
33. 95.8°
35. $B = (\pm 12\sqrt{13})\ \mathbf{i}_x \mp (8/\sqrt{13})\ \mathbf{i}_y$
39. a) -11, b) -11

Chapter 2

5. a) yes b) 180 lb c) 180 lb d) 205 lb e) 205 lb f) yes g) no, these forces are equal and opposite because of what Newton's first law demands of systems in equilibrium
7. 28.3°, 23.75°
9. 1898 lb; 21,040 lb
11. a) 800 lb b) 400 lb
13. F = W/2, T = 3W/2
15. a) 49 N b) 0.144
17. $W_2 = W_1 \sin\theta_1/\sin\theta_2$, $N_1 = W_1\cos\theta_1$, $N_2 = W_2\cos\theta_2$
19. a) $W_1(\sin\theta - \mu_s\cos\theta)$, b) $W_1(\sin\theta - \mu_k\cos\theta)$, c) $W_1(\sin\theta + \mu_s\cos\theta)$
d) $W_1(\sin\theta + \mu_k\cos\theta)$
21. a) $W_1(\sin\theta_1 - \mu_s\cos\theta_1)/(\sin\theta_2 + \mu_s\cos\theta_2)$,
b) $W_1(\sin\theta_1 - \mu_k\cos\theta_1)/(\sin\theta_2 + \mu_k\cos\theta_2)$,
c) $W_1(\sin\theta_1 + \mu_s\cos\theta_1)/(\sin\theta_2 - \mu_s\cos\theta_2)$,
d) $W_1(\sin\theta_1 + \mu_k\cos\theta_1)/(\sin\theta_2 - \mu_k\cos\theta_2)$,
e) $W_1(\sin\theta_1 - \mu_s\cos\theta_1)$, $W_1(\sin\theta_1 - \mu_k\cos\theta_1)$,
$W_1(\sin\theta_1 + \mu_s\cos\theta_1)$, $W_1(\sin\theta_1 + \mu_k\cos\theta_1)$
23. T_1 = 400 lb, T_2 = 346.4 lb, T_3 = 692.8 lb, W = 600 lb

25. a) $\frac{1}{2}$ W csc θ, b) $\frac{1}{2}$ W cot θ, c) No
27. 2.4 m to the right of the knife edge support
29. front wheels, 2333 lb; rear wheels, 1667 lb
31. a) 555.6 lb, b) 576.1 lb, at 39.52° with horizontal
33. a) 518.0 N b) F = 433 N at 114° with + x-axis c) 0.448
35. a) T = 30720 N, b) F_x = -30720 N, F_y = 14110 N
37. T = 4 Mg sin (θ/2)
39. mg $(2Rd - d^2)^{1/2}/(R - d)$
41. a) N_1 = 120 lb, N_2 = 80 lb, b) T = 50.3 lb, c) R_x = 50.3 lb, R_y = 80 lb
43. $N_1 = \frac{1}{2} W (\cos\theta + \frac{2h}{d}\sin\theta)$, $F_{f1} = \frac{1}{2} W \sin\theta (1 + \frac{2h}{d}\tan\theta)$ (right side);
$N_2 = \frac{1}{2} W (\cos\theta - \frac{2h}{d}\sin\theta)$, $F_{f2} = \frac{1}{2} W \sin\theta (1 - \frac{2h}{d}\tan\theta)$ (left side)
45. a) $F = Wd/\ell$, b) $N = W(1 - \frac{d}{\ell})$, c) 150 lb, d) 300 lb
47. a) 42 lb, b) F_x = 36.4 lb, F_y = 9.0 lb
49. sin φ = (3π/4) sin θ
51. a) Only approximately correct b) Prince

Chapter 3
7. a) (1000/π) m due east, b) (1000/π) m due west, c) (1000/π) m due north,
d) 20 m/s, due north e) 20 m/s, due south, f) 20 m/s, due west,
g) $(40\sqrt{2}/\pi)$= 18.01 m/s, northwest, h) $(4\sqrt{2}/5)$ m/s^2, southwest
11. a) a = m/s^2, b = m/s^4 b) $v_x = 32t - 4t^3$ c) $a_x = 32 - 12t^2$ d) 64 m
e) 34.84 m/s f) 33 m/s g) 4 m/s^2
13. $v_x(t) = -\omega x_o \sin\omega t$; $a_x(t) = -\omega^2 x_o \cos\omega t$; - 118.6 cm/s; - 985 cm/s^2
15. a) $9\underset{\sim}{i}_x - 9\underset{\sim}{i}_y$ (m) b) $3\underset{\sim}{i}_x + 15\underset{\sim}{i}_y$ (m/s) c) $18\underset{\sim}{i}_y$ (m/s^2) d) $6\underset{\sim}{i}_x - 16\underset{\sim}{i}_y$ (m)
e) $3\underset{\sim}{i}_x$ (m/s) f) $12\underset{\sim}{i}_y$ (m/s^2)
17. a) x = -8.485 m, y = 4.243 m b) v_x = -79.97 m/s, v_y = -39.99 m/s
c) a_x = 753.7 m/s^2, a_y = -376.9 m/s^2 d) $(x^2/144) + (y^2/36) = 1$
19. a) $v_x = 10\,t + 6\,t^2$, $v_y = 10\,t - 4\,t^3$, $v_z = 25 - 3\,t^2$;
b) $a_x = 10 + 12\,t$, $a_y = 10 - 12\,t^2$, $a_z = -6t$;
c) $v = \sqrt{625 + 50\,t^2 + 120\,t^3 - 35\,t^4 + 16\,t^6}$,
d) $a = \sqrt{200 + 240\,t - 60\,t^2 + 144\,t^4}$,
e) x = 36 cm, y = 4 cm, z = 42 cm, v_x = 44 cm/s, v_y = -12 cm/s,
v_z = 13 cm/s, a_x = 34 cm/s^2, a_y = -38 cm/s^2,
a_z = -12 cm/s^2, v = 47.4 cm/s, a = 52.4 cm/s^2 f) $r = \sqrt{x^2 + y^2 + z^2}$ = 55.4 cm
21. $(2(v_x - v_o)/9\alpha)^{1/2}\,(v_x + 2v_o)$
23. a) 5.58 sec, b) 218.4 ft/s
25. 43.8 ft/s
27. 77.6 ft/s
29. a) 10 sec b) 20 ft/s

31. a) yes b) 2.438 sec. after the brakes are applied c) 61.26 m from the position of the car when the brakes are applied d) 5.0625 m/s^2

33. a) 20,000 ft b) 63.45°

35. a) 45°, b) v_o^2/g

37. a) (50 m, 20.4 m), (75 m, 15.9 m), (150 m, -56.4 m) b) (25 m/s, 0.4 m/s), (25 m/s, - 9.4 m/s), (25 m/s, -38.8 m/s) c) (0, -9.8 m/s^2) in all cases, d) 2.041 sec e) 20.41 m f) 4.082 sec g) 102.0 m

39. a) 144 ft/s, b) 561.2 ft

41. a) 56.25 ft, b) 3.75 sec, c) 300 ft, d) x = 41.75 ft, y = 297.08 ft, e) 12.70 ft/s, f) α = 61.23°

45. a) 182.2 rad/s^2, b) 91.1 rad/s, c) 14.5 revolutions d) 151.3 rad/s

47. a) 75.5 rad/s, b) - 18.45 rad/s^2

49. a) 64 feet, b) 36 feet above the tee, c) v_x = 82.2 ft/s, v_z = -80 ft/s

51. a) 0.80 m/s^2, due north b) 1.490 m/s^2, 12.52° south of due west c) 5.090 m/s^2, 9.04° south of due east

53. a) $v_r = -2a\omega \sin \omega t$, $v_\theta = 2a\omega \cos \omega t$, $v = 2a\omega$,

b) $a_r = -4a\omega^2 \cos \omega t$, $a_\theta = -4a\omega^2 \sin \omega t$, $a = 4a\omega^2$,

c) $v_t = 2a\omega$, $v_n = 0$, d) $a_t = 0$, $a_n = -4a\omega^2$

55. a) a three-leaved rose, b) $v_r = -3b\omega \sin 3\omega t$, $v_\theta = b\omega \cos 3\omega t$,

c) $a_r = -10b\omega^2 \cos 3\omega t$, $a_\theta = -6b\omega^2 \sin 3\omega t$,

d) $v = b\omega\ (1 + 8 \sin^2 3\omega t)^{1/2}$, e) $a = 6b\omega^2\ (1 + \frac{16}{9} \cos^2 3\omega t)^{1/2}$,

f) $v_t = v$, $v_n = 0$, g) $a_t = 12b\omega^2 \sin 6\omega t/(1 + 8 \sin^2 3\omega t)^{1/2}$

$a_n = -b\omega^2\ (10 + 8 \sin^2 3\omega t)/(1 + 8 \sin^2 3\omega t)^{1/2}$

57. a) at a point 2.077 feet radially outward from his starting point and displaced through an angle of -2.623° from his original position on the platform b) at a point 5.548 ft radially outward from the point from which he jumps, and displaced through an angle of -4.742° from his original position on the platform from which he jumps

59. a) $t = d/v'$, b) $x = d(v_o/v')$, c) $\tan \theta = v_o/v'$, d) $v = \sqrt{v_o^2 + v'^2}$

61. Ground speed 291.1 mph, true course 50.44°

Chapter 4

1. 870 lbs

3. 2.84 m/s^2

5. a) 230.4 lb, b) 153.6 lb, c) 192 lb, d) 192 lb

7. a) $a_x = F/(m_1 + m_2)$ b) $Fm_2/(m_1 + m_2)$ c) $a_x = -F/(m_1 + m_2)$ d) $Fm_1/(m_1 + m_2)$

9. a) 1.333 m/s^2 b) 9.333 N c) 5.333 N

11. a,b) 2.933 ft/s^2 c) 15.33 lb d) -2.400 ft/s^2 e) 2.00 lb

13. a) 2.0 m/s^2 b) 0.241

17. 0.160

19. a) $T = g\ (1 + \sin\theta + \mu_k \cos\theta) \cdot mM/(m + M)$

b) $a = g\ (M - m \sin\theta - \mu_k m \cos\theta)/(m + M)$

21. a) W = 20 lb (W moves upward), W = 40 lb (W moves downward) b) W = 18 lb (W moves upward), W = 42 lb (W moves downward)

23. a) -4.16 ft/s b) 10.8 lb c) 2.24 ft/s^2 d) 34.8 lb
25. a) $(m_2 g \sin\theta_2 - m_1 g \sin\theta_1)/(m_1 + m_2)$ b) $m_1 m_2 g (\sin\theta_1 + \sin\theta_2)/(m_1 + m_2)$
27. a) 1.089 m/s^2 b) 43.55 N c) 26.13 N
31. a) $N_1 = (mg/2) - (hma/d)$ b) $N_2 = (mg/2) + (hma/d)$ c) $F_{f1} = (ma/2) - (hma^2/dg)$

d) $F_{f2} = (ma/2) + (hma^2/dg)$ e) $F_{front} = \sqrt{N_1^2 + F_{f1}^2}$, $\tan\theta = F_{f1}/N_1 = a/g$

f) $F_{rear} = \sqrt{N_2^2 + F_{f1}^2}$, $\tan\theta = a/g$ g) $a_{max} = -dg/2h$ Note that a is negative for deceleration and θ refers to the angle between the force vector and the vertical.

33. 1936 lb
35. a) 2.675 m/s b) 3.049 N c) 1.439 sec d) increases
37. 4630 km from the center of the earth. Note that since the earth's radius is 6380 km, this point is in the interior of the earth.
39. a) ω = 0.8 rad/s = 0.127 rps b) No
41. 9.14 rad/s = 1.45 rps
43. $v = \sqrt{\mu g r}$
45. a) 212 ft/s = 144.7 mph b) 7238 lb
47. a) 0.89 m/s b) 16.7 N c) 36.7 N
49. a) 1.75 m/s^2 (up the plane) b) 92 N c) 322 N
51. a) 66,800 ft (12.6 mi) b) 93.2 ft east of the point at which they are aimed by the theory of Section 3.3 c) 0.080°
53. a) $a = g \sin\theta$ b) $N_1 = (m_1+m_2) g \sin\theta$ c) $N_2 = m_1 g \cos^2\theta$

d) $F_f = m_1 g \sin\theta \cos\theta$

55. $T = 36.75$ N, $\mu_k = 0.125$
57. x* = 3/2 units, y* = 6.400 units
59. x* = y* = 0, z* = 17 a/20
61. x* = y* = 0, $z^* = (\rho_1 a^2 - \rho_2 b^2)/(2\rho_1 a + 2\rho_2 b)$

Chapter 5

3. $$\sqrt{\frac{m}{k}} \cdot \int_{x_0}^{x} \left(\frac{1 + (k/mg)^2 x^2}{x_0^2 - x^2}\right)^{1/2} dx = t$$

5. a) 10.87 lb b) 261 ft-lb c) -261 ft-lb d) zero
7. a) 4000 N/m b) 5.0 joule c) 75 joule
9. a) k = 11600 N/m, b = 160000 N/m^3 b) 7800 N c) 550 joule
11. $\frac{1}{2} \mu h^2$ ft-lb
13. 1,832,000 lb (= 916 tons)
15. 401.5 ft-lb/s (0.730 hp); 151.5ft-lb/s (0.275 hp)
17. a) 1.423 kw b) 2.845 kw
19. a) $dyne/cm^3 = gm\ s^{-2}\ cm^{-2}$ b) $\frac{512}{3}$ ergs c) 256 ergs d) No
21. a) $F_x = m\alpha^2 x$, $F_y = F_z = 0$ b) $U_p(x) = -m\alpha^2 x^2/2$ c) $U_k(x) = m\alpha^2 x^2/2$

d) $U_k(t) = m\alpha^2 a^2 e^{-2\alpha t}/2$

23. $A \ln(1 + x) = \mu mgx$
25. 230 ft/s (157 mph)
27. a) $v = P_o v_o/(P_o + mgv_o \sin\theta)$ b) 64.8 ft/s (44.2 mph)
29. $W = \sqrt{2mU_{ko}}\, \Delta v + m(\Delta v)^2/2$
31. a) zero b) $-mg\ell(1 - \cos\theta)$ c) $mg\ell(1 - \cos\theta)$
33. a) 24.25 m/s b) 9.59 m c) 1.25
37. $mg\ell(1 - \cos\theta)/2$
39. a) 4200 joule b) 2940 joule c) 600 joule d) 660 joule
41. a) $\sqrt{2g\ell}$ b) 3mg c) $\sqrt{2g\ell/3}$ d) mg/3
43. a) $\mu_k = m'h/((m+m')d + mh)$ b) 0.394
45. a) 11.82 ft b) 9.41 ft/s
47. a) $s_m = U_o/(mg(\sin\theta + \mu_k \cos\theta))$, where $U_o = \frac{1}{2} k\xi^2$ and $m = w/g$
b) $v_d = (2g(\sin\theta + \mu_k \cos\theta)(s_m - d))^{1/2}$
49. a) $a = (P/2mt)^{1/2}$ b) $F = (Pm/2t)^{1/2}$
51. a) $x = v^2/(2 \mu_s g)$ b) 121 ft c) $x = (v^2/(2 \mu_s g) + vt_r$ d) 174 ft
53. mg/2
55. $F = mg (\sin\theta + \mu_k \cos\theta)$ b) $(1 + \mu_k \cot\theta)^{-1}$
57. $v^2 = 2gh (M - m)/(M + m)$

Chapter 6
1. a) 6190 slug-ft/s b) 73.3 ft/s c) 56.8 ft/s
3. a) No b) The box's initial momentum is almost all transferred to the earth.
5. $v_A = 3.79$ m/s, $v_B = -2.53$ m/s
7. a) 26.7 ft/s b) 30 ft/s, before and after c) 30,000 ft-lb
9. a) 1.40 m/s, 2.34 m/s b) 0.918 m/s, 1.53 m/s c) 25 m/s, 41.7 m/s^2
11. a) 56 ft/s b) 1,568,000 lb/ft c) 50 d) 0.63 ft/s
13. v = 27.1 ft/s, velocity vector lies 69.7° south of west; energy is not conserved
15. $v_A = 13.4$ m/s, $v_B = 6.49$ m/s; collision is not perfectly elastic
17. $v_1 = 2.35$ m/s, $\theta = 68.0°$ below the -x-axis. Collision is inelastic.
23. $v_{1y} = -0.8\, u$, $v_{2x} = 2.7\, u$
25. b) $\cos\phi = d/2r_o$ $d < 2r_o$
27. a) 0.5 m/s b) 0.5 m/s for each, but in opposite directions c) 1.5 joules
d) 1/2
29. $10^8 \underset{\sim}{i}_x + 10^8 \underset{\sim}{i}_y$ cm/s, $10^8 \underset{\sim}{i}_x - 10^8 \underset{\sim}{i}_y$ cm/s
31. a) 4.0 cm/s, to the left b) 1890 erg c) 2.727 cm/s, to the right
33. a) 0.2499 m/s b) 300.0 m/s
35. a) 800 m/s b) 353 m/s
37. 90 ft/s
39. 1.543 kg, 8.4 m/s
41. 27.9 ft/s
47. a) 2×10^7 N b) $m(t) = 100{,}000 - 200\,t$ c) $a = (2 \times 10^7/(100{,}000 - 200\,t)) - g(t)$
49. a) $v_1 = 53.3$ ft/s; $v_2 = 106.6$ ft/s b) $R_1 = 25.5$ yd; $R_2 = 102.0$ yd
c) R = 228 yd; hence he is wrong
51. 158.4 m/s

Chapter 7

1. $\alpha = 1406\ \text{rad/s}^2$, F = 70.3 N
3. 12 kg-m^2
5. a) 1.62 kg-m^2 b) 61.1 N-m c) 106.0 sec d) 1590 rev
9. a) 6.55 kg-m^2 b) 90.97 N c) 4.00 m/s d) 10.00 rad/s
11. a) 12.6 rad/s^2 b) 2.52 m/s^2 c) 30.24 N d) 131.04 N
13. $7\ m\ell^2/12$
15. $m(a^2 + b^2)/12$
17. $3mR^2/10$
19. $2mR^2/3$
21. $3M(R^5 - r^5)/(10(R^3 - r^3))$, where R and r are the radii of the two planar surfaces of the object.
23. a) 1.08 kg-m^2 b) 53,300 joule c) 53,300 joule
25. 182 joule
27. a) 1/2 b) 2/5 c) 1/3 d) 2/7
29. a) 7.96 m/s b) 5.27 m/s^2 c) 52.7 rad/s^2, 35.1 rad/s^2 d) 26.3 N, 28.1 N
31. a) 2.00 m/s^2 b) 6.67 rad/s^2
33. $\alpha = 6.5\ \text{m/s}^2$, T = 4.4 N
39. $\frac{m\ell^2}{6} = 0.21\ \text{km m}^2$
41. $\frac{3}{5}R$
43. 4.08 rps
45. 0.03508 rad/s
47. 0.77 rps
49. a) to the right, $F(1 - \frac{r}{R})/(m + \frac{I}{R^2})$ b) to the left, $-F\,\frac{r}{R}/(m + \frac{I}{R^2})$
    c) $\cos\theta = r/R$
51. a) 40 ft/s b) 80 rad/s c) 350 ft-lb d) 2/7 e) 13.7 ft/s^2, 1.7 lb
53. 235.6 N
55. 1047 joules
57. 2R/5
59. 2172.8 lb-ft, towards center of circle
61. a) 6.283 $\text{kg-m}^2\text{/s}$, in direction of gyro axis b) 1.47 N-m, in horizontal plane, perpendicular to gyro axis c) 0.234 rad/s, vertical

Chapter 8

1. 1.67×10^{-9} N, 490 N
3. $3.435 \times 10^{-8}\ \text{lb-ft}^2\text{/slug}^2$
5. $1.135 \times 10^{-5}\ \text{m/s}^2$
7. 8.17×10^{-6} m
9. 1.86×10^{-49} joules
11. 6.264×10^{7} joule/kg b) 6.263×10^{7} joule/kg c) 4.767×10^{7} joule/kg d) 1.513×10^{7} joule/kg e) 9.834 N/kg f) 9.831 N/kg g) 5.696 N/kg h) 0.574 N/kg
13. a) 2.020×10^{-7} N in -z-direction b) -2.29×10^{-7} joule

17. 6.26×10^{10} joule

19. a) $F = 16\pi^2 G\rho_1\rho_2 r_1^3 r_2^3/9(r_1+r_2)^2$ b) $U_p = -16\pi^2 G\rho_1\rho_2 r_1^3 r_2^3/9(r_1+r_2)$ c) 16 d) 32

23. 5.81×10^{-11}, fractional change -2.91×10^{-11}

25. $\frac{R_e\omega^2}{g}$, larger

27. 0.41 R_e

29. 96.2 min

31. 1.988×10^{30} kg

33. 1.10×10^8 joules, -1.41×10^7 joules

35. 686 ft, 64.8 sec

37. a) 5.77 m/s b) 30.32 joules

39. 2 N

41. 1.77×10^{10} kg, no

Chapter 9

1. a) 5 meters b) 0.13 cps c) 7.9 s d) 0.64 $(rad/s)^2$
3. a) 4.8 cm b) 7.5 rad/s c) 1.19 cps d) $\pi/4$ rad e) 0.838 sec f) 11250 dyne/cm
5. a) 12.25 rad/s b) 0.513 sec c) 0.1636 m d) 0.0214 rad e) $x = 0.1636 \sin (12.25t + 0.0214)$
7. a) $x = \pm 0.2828$ m b) ± 3.20 m/s c) $\pi/4$, $3\pi/4$, $5\pi/4$, $7\pi/4$ rad
9. a) 0.807 cps b) 0.1512 m
13. Amplitude, 3.175, phase constant 79.1°
15. a) 30.56 N-m/rad b) 1.209 kg-m^2 c) $\phi = (\pi/3) \sin (5.027t + \pi/2)$ radians
17. 2.41 sec
19. $f > \sqrt{g/A}/2\pi$
21. 1.44 cps, 0.70 sec
25. $\phi = 0.19 \sin (3.13\,t + 0.60)$
27. a) $A \sin (10\pi t + \frac{\pi}{2})$ b) $\frac{\dot{v}_o}{\omega} \sin (10\pi t)$ c) $2.006 \sin (10\pi t + 1.49)$
29. 0.61 cps, 1.64 sec; 0.50 cps, 2 sec; 0.58 cps, 1.74 sec
35. a) $k' = k_1 + k_2$ b) $k' = k_1k_2/(k_1 + k_2)$
43. 12.34 kg/s
47. a) 60.0 cps b) 1.407×10^{-4} m c) 1.900×10^{-4} m d) 3.454×10^{-4} m e) 6.608×10^{-4}m f) 3.193×10^{-3}m g) 6.359×10^{-3}m h) 3.169×10^{-2}m

Chapter 10

1. a) $y(x,t) = 0.5 \sin 2\pi((x/8) - 20\,t)$ ft b) 160 ft/s c) 44.4 ft/s, 5583 ft/s^2 d) 0.080 lb
3. a) 1.257×10^5 rad/s, 379.6 m^{-1} b) 1.257×10^5 rad/s, 4.19×10^{-4} m^{-1} c) 2.08×10^9 rad/s, 6.28×10^6 m^{-1} d) 1.885×10^{15} rad/s, 6.28×10^6 m^{-1}
5. a) 0.72 m b) 270 rad/s c) 3.60 m^{-1} d) 1.745 m e) 43.0 Hz f) 75 m/s
7. a) 0.15 m, 12 Hz, 2.4 m b) 28.8 m/s c) -5.65 m/s, 738 m/s^2 d) 82.9 N
9. 3.0 kg
15. 400 m/s
19. 0.201 watts
23. a) 292.5 Hz b) 222.7 Hz
25. 69.4 ft/s
27. 41.5°, 20.7 sec

29. a) 497.9 Hz b) 562.0 Hz c) 64.1 Hz
31. $\lambda = 4L, 4L/3, 4L/5, 4L/7, \ldots; f = v/4L, 3v/4L, 5v/4L, \ldots$
33. c) Yes
37. a) Yes, at frequencies such that $f = nv/2\ell$ where v is the speed of sound, $\ell = 8.0$ m is the width of the room, and n = 1,2,3,4,5,......etc. b) By covering the walls with sound absorbing materials so as to minimize reflections that result in standing waves.

Chapter 11

3. a) 18,330 N b) zero c) 18,330 N, directed normally inward, on the outer surface d) 18,330 N, normally inward e) 18,330 N, normally outward f) zero
5. a) 1.013×10^5 N/m^2 b) 14,700 N/m^2 c) 1.160×10^5 N/m^2 d) 1.013×10^5 N/m^2 (acting upward) e) 72,160 N.,(acting downward) e) 14,700 N/m^2
7. a) 61.12 lb/in^2 b) 65.70 lb/in^2
9. a) 6.50 lb/in^2 b) 33,700 lb c) 42,100 lb d) 3.25 lb/in^2 e) 16,850 lb f) 10,525 lb
11. 4.517×10^7 lb/ft^2
13. P_g = 16006 lb/in^2 = 1089 atm. Assumption of incompressibility in Problem 10 is quite good.
15. 1.123 gm/cm^3
17. 6.58 gm/cm^3
19. a) 39,200 dynes, straight up b) 31,360 dynes, straight down c) 35,280 dynes normal to each face (inward) d) 7,840 dynes, straight up e) yes
21. a) 17,640 lb b) 58,810 lb
23. 232,300 dynes, corresponding to a "mass" of 237.0 grams
27. y_0 = 1500 cm = 15 m
31. 0.857 r
33. 48,000 N/m^2; 234,000 kg
35. a) 29.0 ft/s b) 65.25 ft/s c) 5.02 lb/in^2
37. 32.1 min
39. 0.322 g
41. 736.7 torr
45. a) $W = 8\pi\gamma(r^2 - r_o^2)$ b) 15,700 erg or 0.00157 joule

Chapter 12

1. 176.4°F
3. -38°F, 675°F
5. 14.5°C
7. 27.9 ft^3
9. 1554 w (2.08 hp), 68.4 min
11. 472°C
13. 15.9 gallons
15. 22 g/s
17. $$\frac{T_A(T_{AB}-T_B)(T_{BC}-T_C) + T_C(T_B-T_{BC})(T_A-T_{AB})}{(T_{AB}-T_B)(T_{BC}-T_C) + (T_B-T_{BC})(T_A-T_{AB})}$$
19. 15.9°C
21. 50.006 cm
23. 19.23 g/cm^3
25. 3.87 kg
27. 100°C
31. 1.12×10^3 BTU

33. $T_o - T = (\Delta Q/\Delta T)\ \ell n\ (r/r_o)/(2\pi K)$, where $\Delta Q/\Delta T$ is the heat flow per unit length
37. 11.6 hrs
45. $\alpha = (\alpha_1 \ell_1 + \alpha_2 \ell_2)/(\ell_1 + \ell_2)$

Chapter 13
1. a) 1545 ft-lb/mole °F b) 1.986 btu/mole °F c) 2.732×10^{26}
3. 2.52×10^{-3} ℓ
5. 5.21 atm, 5.91×10^{22}
7. 13.8 atm
9. 16.8 g
13. 7.30 g, 0.917 ℓ
15. 70.4 cm^3
17. 1.50×10^4 g
19. 425 km
21. a) 2.73×10^{25} b) 724 g
23. a) 2.2 atm b) 0.406 moles c) 6.16 cal/mole-°C
27. a) P_i = 14.9 atm, P_f = 3.73 atm b) 10,480 joules
29. 16.8°C, 10.1°C
31. $\eta = 0.062$
33. 0.02
35. 1944 m/s, 4575°C
37. 1.63 moles, 9.83×10^{23} molecules, 1.26×10^4 joules
39. a) 14.8 atm b) 322°K, 15.9 atm c) 8058 joules d) 645°K
e) 20,103 joules (4802 cal), 12,045 joules f) 600°K g) 577 joules
43. 484 m/s, 8.4×10^{22}
47. a) 343 m/s b) 263 m/s c) 195 m/s
49. $c_v = 3R$, $c_p = 4R$, $\gamma = 1.333$
51. a) 0.997×10^{-20} joules
b) 6.75×10^{-20} joules

Chapter 14
1. a) 1/16 b) 5/16 c) 5/8
3. a), c), d) reversible b), e) irreversible
5. 0.4
7. 757.9 joules (181.0 cal)
9. 2285 joules, ΔQ_{AB} = 45.1 liter-atm, ΔQ_{CD} = -22.6 liter-atm, 0.5
11. 1.65×10^7 cal, 2.2×10^6 joules
13. 80.2 btu/s
15. 12,937 joules, 2937 joules
17. lower T_1
21. a) 0.535 b) 5580 joule/sec
23. a) No, since its operating efficiency is less than that of a Carnot engine operating between the same temperatures b) 56.73 joule/sec c) 68.73 watts
25. 312 cal/°K
29. a) -5470 joule b) 5470 joule c) zero d) zero e) zero
31. a) +83,660 joule b) -83,66 joule c) +289.8 joule/°K d) zero
e) +289.8 joule/°K
33. 9.7 joules/°K
37. a) $\Delta U = 0$, $\Delta Q = \Delta W = nRT_o\ \ell n\ (x/x_o) + F_f\ (x-x_o)$ b) $\Delta Q' = -nRT_o\ \ell n\ (x/x_o)$, $\Delta U' = F_f\ (x-x_o)$, $\Delta W' = -nRT_o\ \ell n\ (x/x_o) - F_f\ (x-x_o)$ c) $\Delta S = nR\ \ell n\ (x/x_o) + F_f\ (x-x_o)/T_o$ d) $\Delta S' = -nR\ \ell n\ (x-x_o)$ e) $\Delta S + \Delta S' = F_f\ (x-x_o)/T_o$

Chapter 15

1. 1.076×10^6 N
3. $y = -x^2/2$, where x and y are in cm.
5. a) 0.002 N b) 0.2 N c) 8×10^{-7} N
7. 15.96 N, the nuclear forces between the protons are attractive.
9. 1.88×10^{16} electrons
11. 13.41 m/sec
13. a) $F = \pm 1.618\, \underset{\sim}{i}_x - 0.560\, \underset{\sim}{i}_y$ N b) zero
15. $F_x = 2kQqa/(a^2 + y^2)^{3/2}$, $F_y = 0$
17. $F_x = 4kQqax/(x^2 - a^2)^2$, $F_y = 0$
19. 894.5 coul
21. 35 at. % Zn., 65 at. % In.
25. 2.21×10^{17} kg/m^3, 8.38×10^{24} coul/m^3

Chapter 16

1. 4.9×10^{-9} coul
3. zero
5. 4.77×10^{-10} coul/cm^3, 1.25×10^{-7} coul
7. 4.42×10^{-6} coul
9. -1.8×10^{-6} joules
13. 5.76×10^{11} N/coul, 5.03×10^6 mph
15. 3.33×10^{-8} coul
17. 66.7 cm
19. 0.477 m, 4.77×10^5 volts, 7.63×10^{-14} joules, 4.77×10^5 eV
21. b) $2mg\ell\,(1-\cos\theta) + Q^2/8\pi\varepsilon_o\ell \sin\theta$
23. 4.37×10^{-18} joule, or 27.3 eV
27. a) 0.899 joule b) 0.9936 joule c) 0.01269 joule d,e) same as b,c)
29. a) 6.24×10^{-4} N-m b) 3.60×10^{-4} joule
37. $\frac{\sigma_o}{2\varepsilon_o}\left[\sqrt{x^2 + R^2} - x - R\,\ell n\left(\frac{\sqrt{x^2 + R^2} + R}{x}\right)\right]$
39. 5.55×10^4 m/sec
41. $[V_o e^{-\mu r} \times (1 + \mu r)/r^2]\, \underset{\sim}{i}_r$, $-\varepsilon_o \mu^2 V_o e^{-\mu r}/r$
43. E proportional to $1/r$, ρ proportional to $1/r^2$
45. $\frac{\sigma}{2\varepsilon_o}\left(\sqrt{R^2 + x^2} - x\right)$
49. -2.30×10^{-10} joules, -3.46×10^{-13} joules
51. a) $E(x) = \alpha x^3/3\varepsilon_o$, b) $V(x) - V(o) = -\alpha x^4/12\varepsilon_o$, where V(o) is the potential at the plane x = 0

Chapter 17

1. 0.02 μf

3. a) 2.83 mm b) 8500 volts

5. a) 1.085×10^{-9} f/m b) 14,600 volts

7. 30 volts/m

9. 7.07×10^{-4} f, 0.707 coul, 1.39×10^{-15} coul/m^2, 1.57×10^{-4} volts/m

11. 8.01×10^{-8} coul

13. 1.2×10^{-5} coul, 3.6×10^{-5} coul, 24 volts, 12 volts, 12 volts

15. 2 μf, 1 μf

21. 0.75¢, 1.875×10^{-5}¢

23. 9.18×10^{60} r^2 inside, 9.18×10^{-30} r^{-4} outside, 1.38×10^{-13} joules, 1.20×10^{27} joules

25. a) $r<r_1$ $E = 0$, $r_1<r<r_1 + x$ $E = q_1/2\pi\varepsilon_o r\ell$, $r_1 + x < r$ $E = -q_1/2\pi\varepsilon_o r\ell$

    b) $r<r_1$ $u_E = 0$, elsewhere $u_E = q^2/8\pi^2\varepsilon_o r^2\ell^2$

    c) $(q_1^2/4\pi\varepsilon_o\ell^2)\ \ell n(x/r_1)$ d) $q_1^2/4\pi\varepsilon_o\ell^2 x$

29. a) 8.33 volts b) 2/3 density of free charge on plates c) 1.88×10^{-3}, 6.25×10^{-4} joules

31. zero on front and back, -3.50×10^{-7} coul/m^2 on all others

33. 8.47×10^{10}

37. a) 3.26×10^{-4} μf/m b,c) r<2 cm D = 0, P = 0; 2 cm<r< 3 cm D = 0, P = 0; 3 cm<r< 5 cm $D = \frac{\lambda}{2\pi r}$, $P = \frac{\lambda}{3\pi r}$; 5 cm<r< 6 cm D = 0, P = 0; 6 cm<r D = 0, P = 0 where $\lambda = 1.08 \times 10^{-7}$ coul/m d) σ (3 cm) $= 1.26 \times 10^{-7}\ \frac{\text{coul}}{\text{m}^2}$,

    σ (5 cm) $= 2.29 \times 10^{-7}\ \frac{\text{coul}}{\text{m}^2}$ e) 1.47×10^{-5} joules/m

39. 10897 $\frac{\text{volts}}{\text{m}}$, 66.6° to normal

Chapter 18

1. 1.87×10^{21}

3. a) 6.36×10^7 amp/m^2 b) 4.65×10^{-3} m/s

5. a) 2 b) 27 c) 1/2

7. 1.2 ohms

9. 2.83×10^{-6} ohms

11. 509 ohms, 2040 ohms

13. 4×10^{-6} m^2

15. 8.89×10^{-6} coul/m^2

17. a) 8.5×10^{-7} m^2 b) 0.1362 ohms

19. 0.972 amps, 3500 joules

21. 0.909 amps, 121 ohms

23. 18.33 ohms, 1.98×10^4 joules, 0.017¢

25. 1.5 hp

27. 6.66 ohms

29. R, 2R, R/2, 3R, R/3, 2R/3, 3R/2

31. 9 ohms
33. 1 ohm
35. $I_1 = 2$ amps, $I_2 = 4$ amps, $I_3 = 2$ amps
37. a) $2 - 4I_1 + 3I_2 = 0$ b) $3 + 3I_1 - 5I_2 = 0$ c) $I_1 = 1.73$ amps, $I_2 = 1.64$ amps
d) 3.46 watts e) 0.024 watts
41. $\mathcal{E}/(R + R_i/n)$, $R\mathcal{E}/(R + R_i/n)$
43. a) 0.345 amps b) 0.517 watts, 0.690 watts c) 0.0119 watts, 0.0059 watts, 1.189 watts d) 1.466 volts, 1.983 volts
49. b) 3.99997×10^7 ohms, 1.5×10^{-4} volts
53. 6.91, 1.49×10^{-7} coul, 3.75×10^{-7} amps
55. b) 4×10^{-5} coul c) 4×10^{-4} joules d) 2×10^{-4} joules e) joule heating

Chapter 19

1. $F = 1.037 \times 10^{-3}$ N, in the yz-plane at 135° to the y- axis
3. 2500 m/s, along +z-direction
7. 0.36 N in +z-direction
9. 1.14×10^{-4} N/amp-m
11. 5.09×10^{-12} N perpendicular to $\underset{\sim}{v}$ and $\underset{\sim}{B}$
13. 10^4 volts/m perpendicular to $\underset{\sim}{v}$ and $\underset{\sim}{B}$
15. 0.0124 weber
19. 0.5 N/m
21. a) 31.1 amp-m^2 b) 6.46 N-m
23. $\pi\omega\sigma R^4/4$
27. $(\mu_o i^2/\pi m)\ \ell n(\frac{d-a}{a})$
29. $1.43\ \mu_o I/L$
31. $\mu_o I\theta(r_2-r_1)/4\pi r_2 r_1$
33. $\mu_o I/2a$
35. 10^{-5} webers/m^2 into paper at P_1, 3×10^{-5} webers/m^2 into paper at P_2
39. $(\mu_o IL^2/2\pi(z^2 + \frac{L^2}{4})(z^2 + \frac{L^2}{2})^{1/2}$
41. rectangular
43. i) $r<r_1$ $B = 0$; $r_1<r<r_2$ $B = \mu_o I(r^3-r_1^3)/2\pi r(r_2^3-r_1^3)$; $r>r_2$ $B = \mu_o I/2\pi r$
ii) $r<r_1$ $B = 0$; $r_1<r<r_2$ $B = \mu_o I(r^4-r_1^4)/2\pi r(r_2^4-r_1^4)$; $r>r_2$ $B = \mu_o I/2\pi r$
45. 22
47. "Ideally" zero, but in this case actually 3.59×10^{-5} weber/m^2
49. 1.11×10^{-4} N/m
51. 1.02 cm
53. 7.61 cm, 0.744 webers/m^2, 1.4×10^5 m/s

Chapter 20

1. a) 0.08 volts b) 20.0 volts
3. 2.1 volts, 1.47 watts
5. a) 0.0251 volts b) 0.0399 volts/m c) 3.15×10^{-4} joules

7. a) $NA'\mu_o nI_o \omega\cos\omega t$ b) $(A'\mu_o nI_o \omega\cos\omega t)/R'$ c) $(A'\mu_o nI_o \omega\cos\omega t)^2 N/R'$
11. 3.14 volts
13. 0.054 weber/m^2
15. 0.0267 weber/m^2
17. a) 0.0452 v/m, b) 0.0353 v/m, c) 0.0565 v/m,at the turns of the coil.
19. a) b→a b) a→b c) a→b
21. 6.28×10^{-4} henry, 0.0628 volts
23. 4.74×10^{-2} henry, 142 volts
25. 1.77×10^{-3} henry
27. 0.267 sec, 1 amp/sec
29. 0.9933
31. 0.5% due to self induced emf, 99.5% across resistor 0.499988 amp
33. a) 360 amp/sec b) 5.4 volts c) 4.32×10^{-6} joules d) 0.0144 watts
35. 3.61 joules, 100 volts
37. $r<r_1$ $\mu_o I^2/16\pi$, $r_1<r<r_2$ $(\mu_o I^2/4\pi)\ \ell n\ (r_2/r_1)$
39. E = cB
41. 0.0142 henry
43. 150 volts
45. a) zero b) 1.03° c) 6.81° d) 35.6° e) 82.1°

Chapter 21

1. a) 1.0×10^6 amp/m b) 1000 amp
3. 1.51 amp-m^2
5. 4.12×10^{23}, 4.77×10^{23} atoms
7. a) 1500 amp/m b) 0.379 webers/m^2 c) 3×10^5 amp/m d) 240 amp-m
9. a) 40,000 amp/m, 0.050283 weber/m^2 b) 14.4 amp/m c) 11.31 amp
   d) 40,000 amp/m, 0.050265 weber/m^2
11. a) 0.0253h b) 18.97h
13. 1.37×10^{-3} weber/amp-m
15. a) 1.60×10^{-4} amp/m b) -8.59×10^{-5} amp/m c) 1.64×10^{-4} amp/m
17. a) 83.80° b) 89.52° c) 89.956°
19. $e^{2p_m B/kT}$
21. 8.99×10^{-24} amp-m^2
25. a) 29.32 weber/m^2 in both cases b) 2.333×10^7 amp/m c) 6.67×10^5 amp/m

Chapter 22

1. 2828 volts, 0.01 sec, 2828 sin 628t
3. 12 volts, no
5. 5.31 Hz, 0.03 sec, 0.498 amp
7. a) 7.54 ohms b) 75.4 ohms c) 754 ohms d) current lags voltage by 90° at all frequencies
9. a) 9.11 amp b) 123.6 volts c) 109.3 volts d) current lags voltage by 48.5°
11. a) 2.764 amp b) 53.3° c) 250.94 volts d) 85.26° e) 165.8 volts
13. a) 105.7 ohms b) 102.7 ohms c) 0.6815 amp d) 76.3° current lags emf
   e) 17.04 volts f) 205.5 volts g) 135.6 volts

15. a) 0.796 h, b) 1.99×10^{-13} f, c) 2×10^{-3} volts, d) 8.91×10^{-4} volts, e) -63.5°
17. 486 Hz, 5×10^{-4} sec
21. 5.37 amp, 0.89, 1
23. 2046 ohms, 0.0538 amp, 0.0829 amp, 0.0292 amp
25. 188.5 ohms, 67.1 volts
27. 10 ohms, 1.26×10^{7} ohms
29. $e^{-(R/2L)t}\left[Ae^{-((R/2L)^2 - 1/LC)^{1/2}t} + Be^{+((R/2L)^2 - 1/LC)^{1/2}t}\right]$
33. 45.6 ohms, 3.52 h, 0.354 watts
37. 5×10^{5} ohms, 9.99×10^{4} ohms, 9055 ohms
39. $\frac{1}{2}(I_1^2 + I_o^2)/R, \sqrt{(I_1^2 + I_o^2)/2}, R\sqrt{(I_1^2 + I_o^2)/2}$

Chapter 23
1. 0.443 amp
3. 2.22×10^{-8} weber/m^2
5. 26.6 amp/m^2
7. $-\frac{1}{2}\varepsilon_o\mu_o r E_o \omega \sin\omega t$
9. $-(C\omega\, \Delta V_o \sin\omega t)$
13. 2.56 sec
15. d) No e) The solutions of the second order equation allow us to superpose waves traveling in opposite directions.
17. 1.257×10^{-3} cm, 2.39×10^{13} Hz, $B = 3 \times 10^{10} E_o \cos 5000\,(z - (3 \times 10^{10})t)\, \underset{\sim}{i}_y$
19. 4.00×10^{4} cm
21. 106 volts/m, 3.55×10^{-7} webers/m^2
23. a) 1.67×10^{-6} webers/m^2 b) 332 watts/m^2
25. a) 2.52 v/m b) 8.39×10^{-9} w/m^2 c) 0.419 v/m d) 9500 w
27. a) 0.0346 v/m b) 0.01095 v/m c) 0.00490 v/m
29. 2.31×10^{-7} volts/m
31. a) 0.461 kg-m/s b) increase
33. 410 Hz

Chapter 24
1. a) 4.69×10^{-7} m b) 0.469 micron c) 469 nm d) 4690 Å e) 21330
3. 0.0360
5. 14°
7. $-\underset{\sim}{v}$
13. 6342 Å, 4.73×10^{14} Hz, 4.73×10^{14} Hz, 3356 Å
15. a) 1.333 b) 0.750 c) 1.418 d) 0.705
17. a) 24.3° b) 53.2°
19. 2.42 mi, 1.15 mi
21. a) 0.11 rad, b) 3625 Å c) 1
23. 43.9°, yes
25. a) 1.41 b) lower c) higher
27. 0.19 cm
29. internally reflected
31. 2.04% 97.96%

33. b) no c) 1.12
35. emerges from the opposite face, 30°
37. $\cos\theta = n_p/n_g$
39. 8 ft
41. a) 28.656° b) 29.783° c) 1.127° d) zero
43. a) 40.330° b) 35.661° c) 39.079° d) 33.158°

Chapter 25
1. a) 13.06 cm b) 0.20 mm
3. a) 7.45 cm b) 41.1 cm
5. a) 28.92 cm b) 31.64 cm c) -36.82 cm (on same side of surface as object) d) 28.92 cm
7. a) 32.00 cm, 20.000 cm b) 180.0 cm c) 16.98 cm
11. a) 8.89 cm b) 24.83 cm c) -75.0 cm d) -21.33 cm e) a,b) convergent c,d) divergent
13. a) 19.64 cm b) 23.57 cm
15. 15.0 cm, -140 cm
17. a) R/(n(n-1)) b) nR/(n-1), measured from the center of curvature of the sphere in both cases
19. a) 357 mm b) 270 mm
21. a) $p = 2n_1r/[2n_3-(n_1+n_2)]$ b) $q = n_2r/[2n_3-(n_1+n_2)]$
25. a) 16.61 cm to the right of lens B b) virtual c) 0.530
27. a) 0.0227 mph b) 0.476 mph
29. 99.2
31. 3.33, 7.00 cm
33. nr from center of sphere
35. a) f:15.30 b) f:7.68 c) f:3.90 d) f:1.89
37. In the liquid, 52.5 cm from the lens
39. a) x = 30.12 cm b) 8.00 cm above the bottom of the tube c) 6.00 cm below the bottom of the tube
41. 59.87 cm
43. a) 10.91 cm b) -192.0 cm c) 11.54 cm on opposite side d) 97.96 cm from lens, on the same side as object
45. 39.3 mm, 2.50 mm, should be reduced to half the former value
47. a) 82.5 mm b) 165 mm c) f:1.9
49. a) 28.7 m b) f:11.3
51. 8.6806 cm b) 9.2693 cm c) 0.1270 cm d) 0.1356 cm e) 0.0656 cm

Chapter 26
1. a) incoherent b) coherent c) incoherent d) coherent e) coherent
3. 0.18 cm
5. a) 5.28×10^{-3} cm b) 158 cm
7. a) 5520 Å b) 0.092 cm c) 0.069 cm
9. a) 3950 Å b) 1.897 c) 0.319
11. 0.00258°
13. 48.5 per cm
15. a) 0.125 cm b) 0.074 cm
19. 64.2 cm
21. 5.98 Å
23. a) 509.14° or 8.8862 rad b) 0.2170 c) 0.04707 d) 10.62 cm
27. a) 15.31° b) 31.87° c) 52.37°
29. 4642 Å

31. b) X-rays
35. 7.46 m
37. a) 328 m b) No
39. a) 772 m b) Yes
41. 0.75 I_o
43. a) 58.93° b) parallel to the surface of the glass c) 31.07° d) 90.00° e) partially polarized
45. a) 53.12° b) 56.31° c) 62.12° d) 68.34° e) 74.48°
47. 0.987 cm, 1.38

Chapter 27

3. 0.333 c
5. 0.866 c
7. -1578 sec
9. x' = 62.6 m, y' = z' = 0, t' = -1.61×10^{-7} sec
11. 3.89×10^{-14} km
13. 0.999999995
15. 0.99993, 0.999999998
25. 6.82×10^{-13} cm, $2.97 \times 10^{+17}$ kg/m^3, 5.36×10^9 tons/in^3
27. 0.268, 0.0000019
29. 0.21
31. a) 5.56×10^{-9} g b) 0.405×10^{-3} volts

Chapter 28

1. $c_1 = 8\pi h/c^3$, $c_2 = h$
3. 6.412×10^6 joules/hr
5. 3621 Å
7. 0.851 eV
9. 3.13 eV
11. 4.84×10^{20} Hz, 6.199×10^{-13} m, 1.07×10^{-21} joule-s/m
15. $v_e/v_n = 1839$
17. 6.805 eV
19. $I(\lambda) = \frac{8\pi ch}{\lambda^5} (e^{hc/\nu kT} - 1)^{-1}$
23. 2817 eV, 2.55×10^{-13} m
25. a) 5040 Å b) 4500 Å source c) 0.295 eV
29. 5175°K
31. Potential energy is constant, independent of position.
33. 5.3×10^{-20} kg-m/sec, 3.16×10^6 m/sec

78 79 80 9 8 7 6 5 4 3 2 1

ISBN 0-06-364108-9